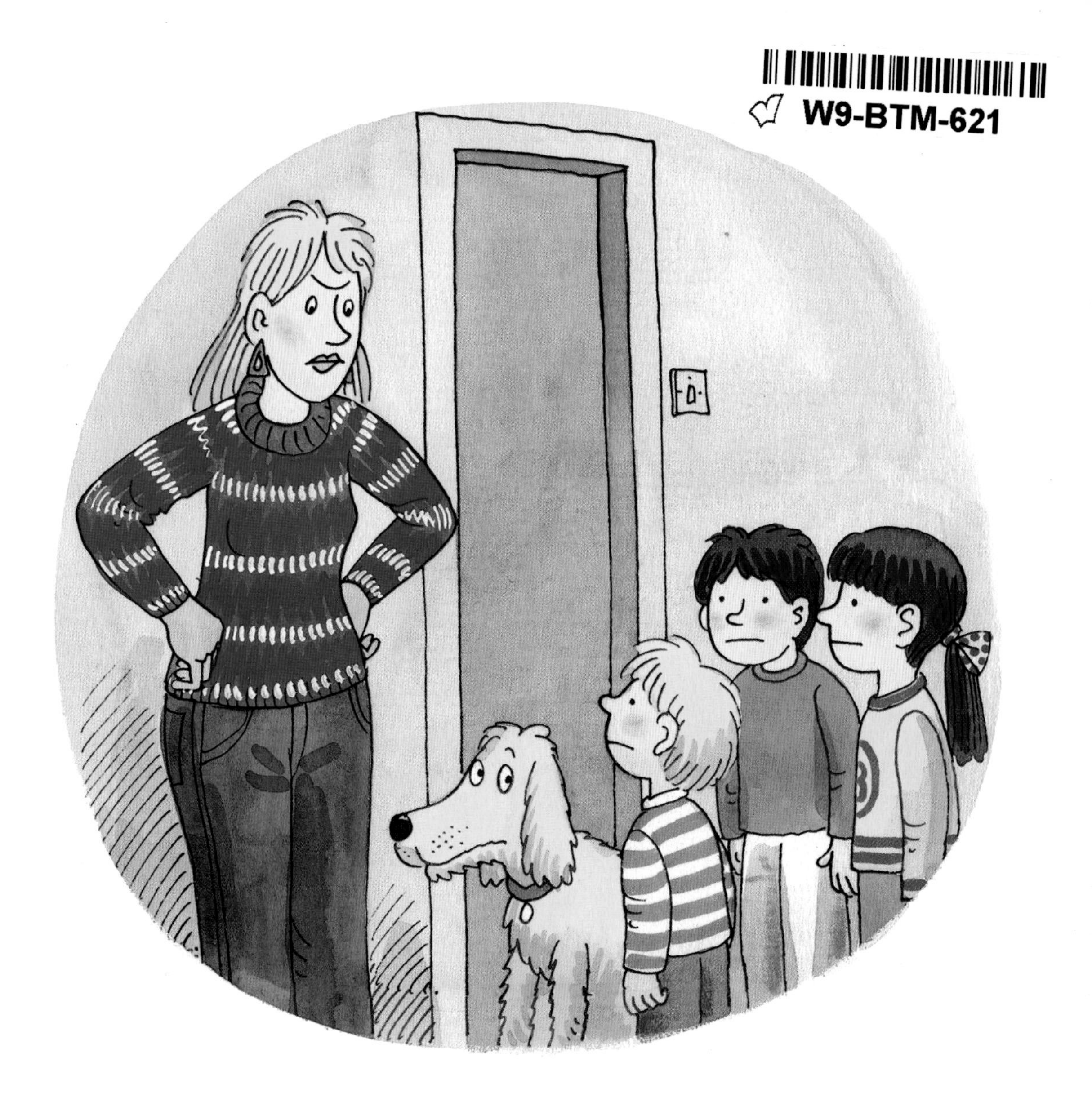

Mum was cross.

"Who did that?" she said.

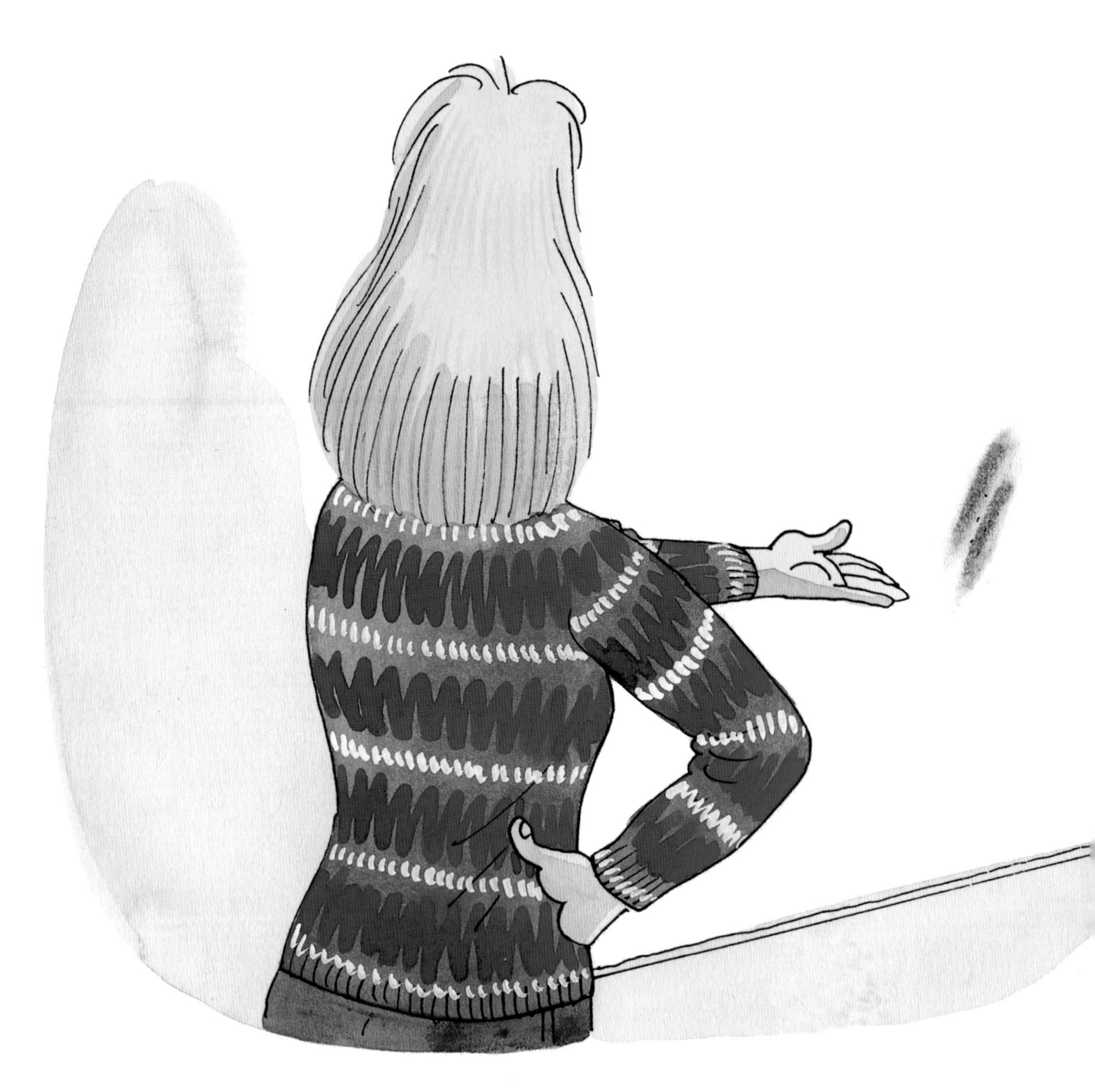

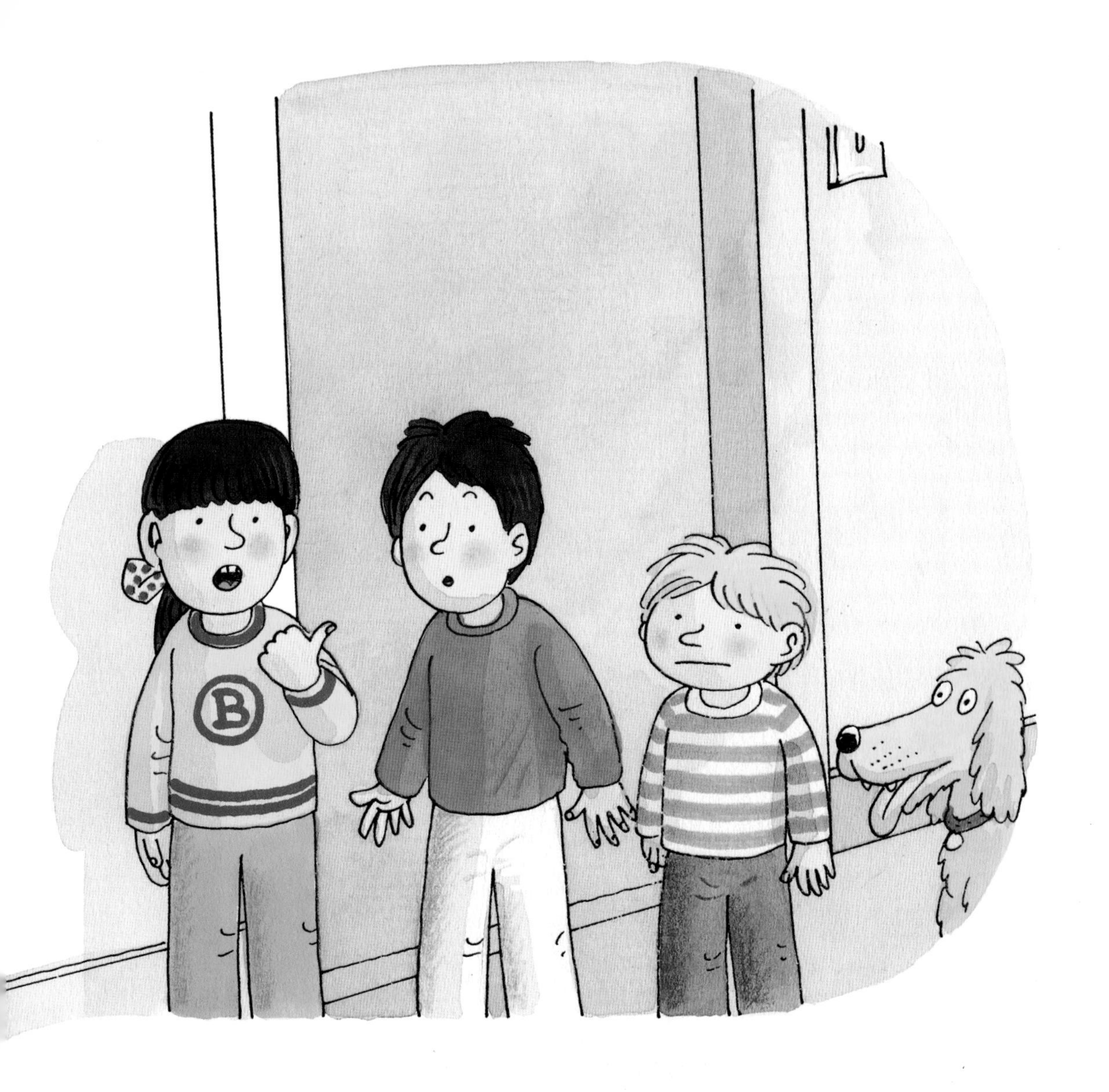

"It was Chip," said Biff.

"It was Kipper," said Chip.

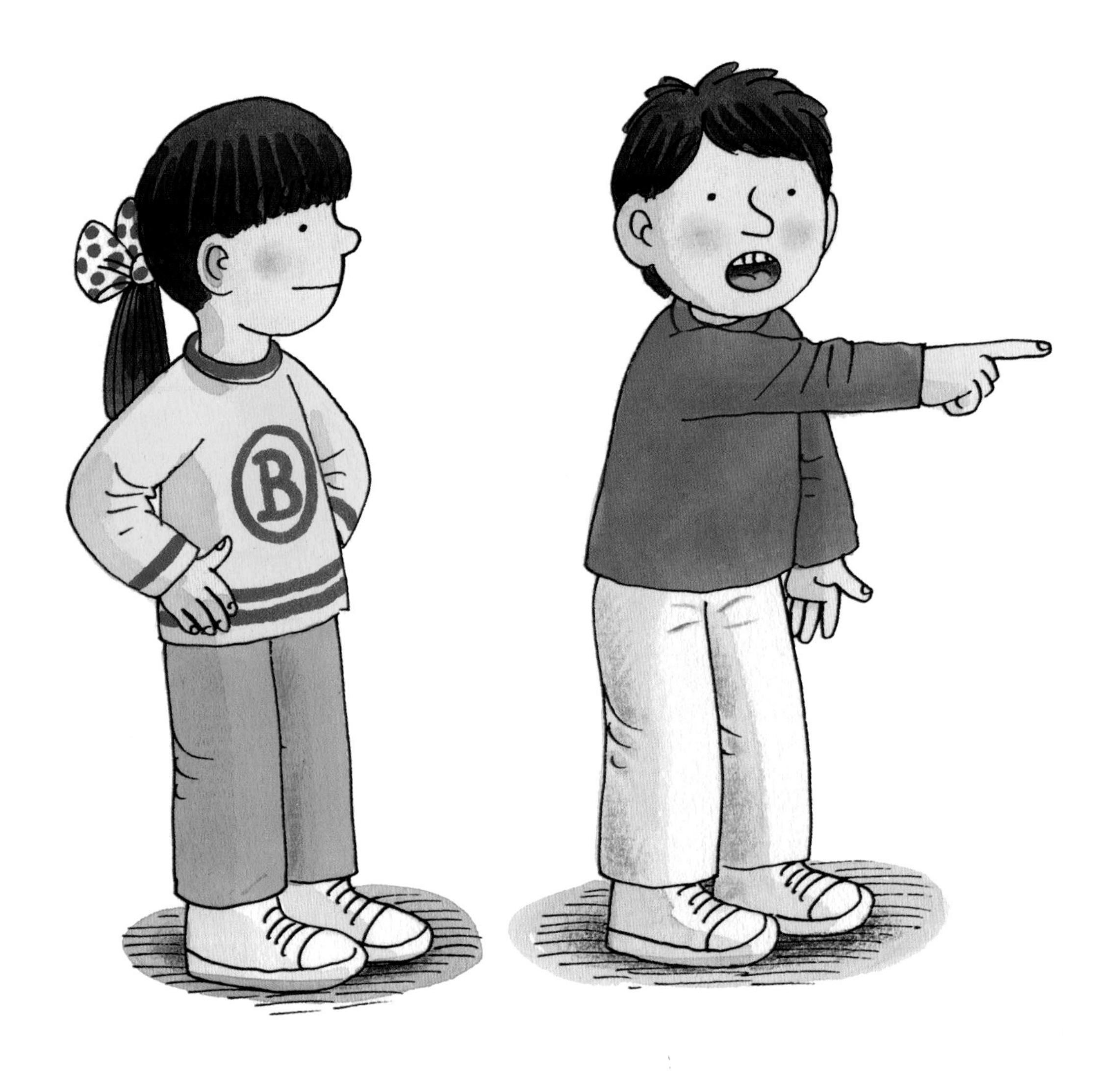

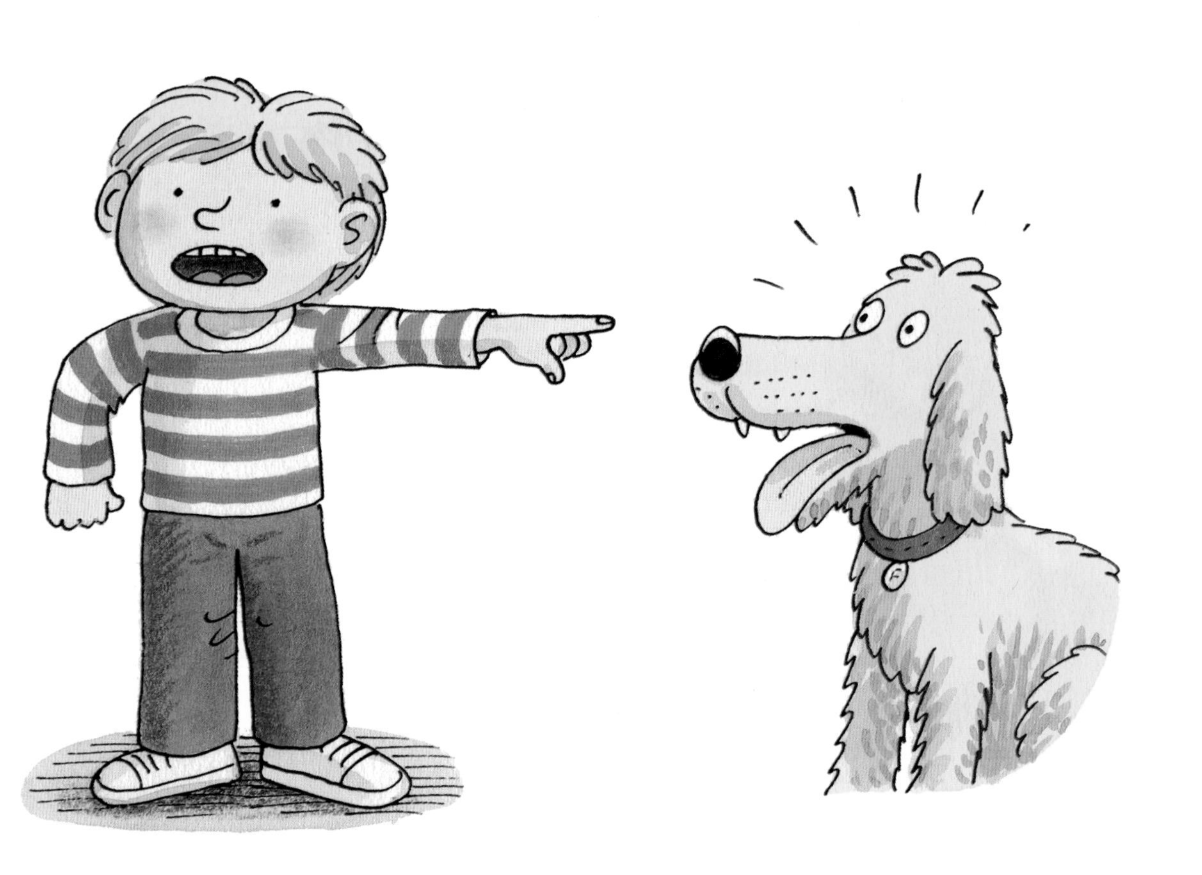

"It was Floppy," said Kipper.

"It was Floppy," said Biff.

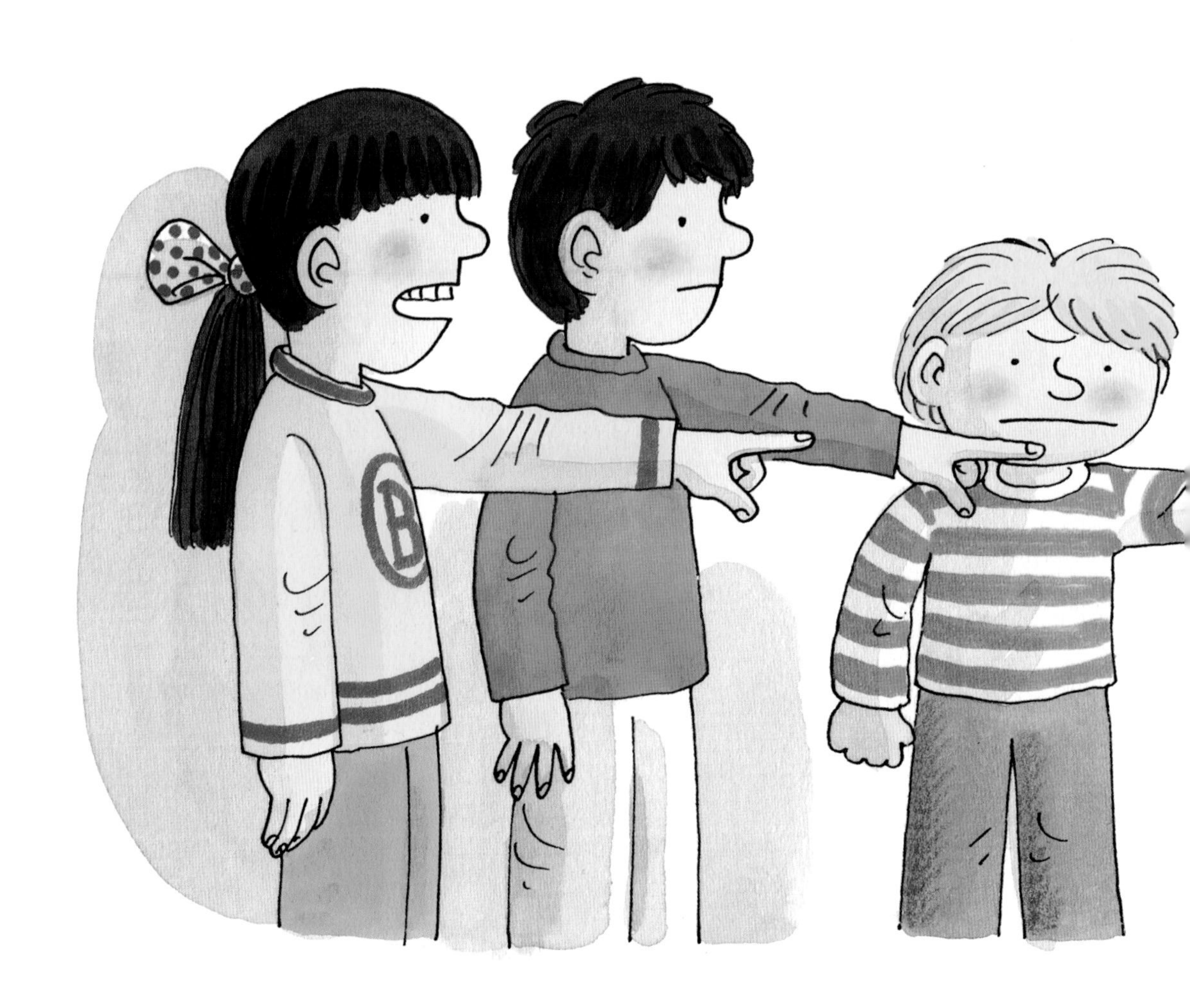

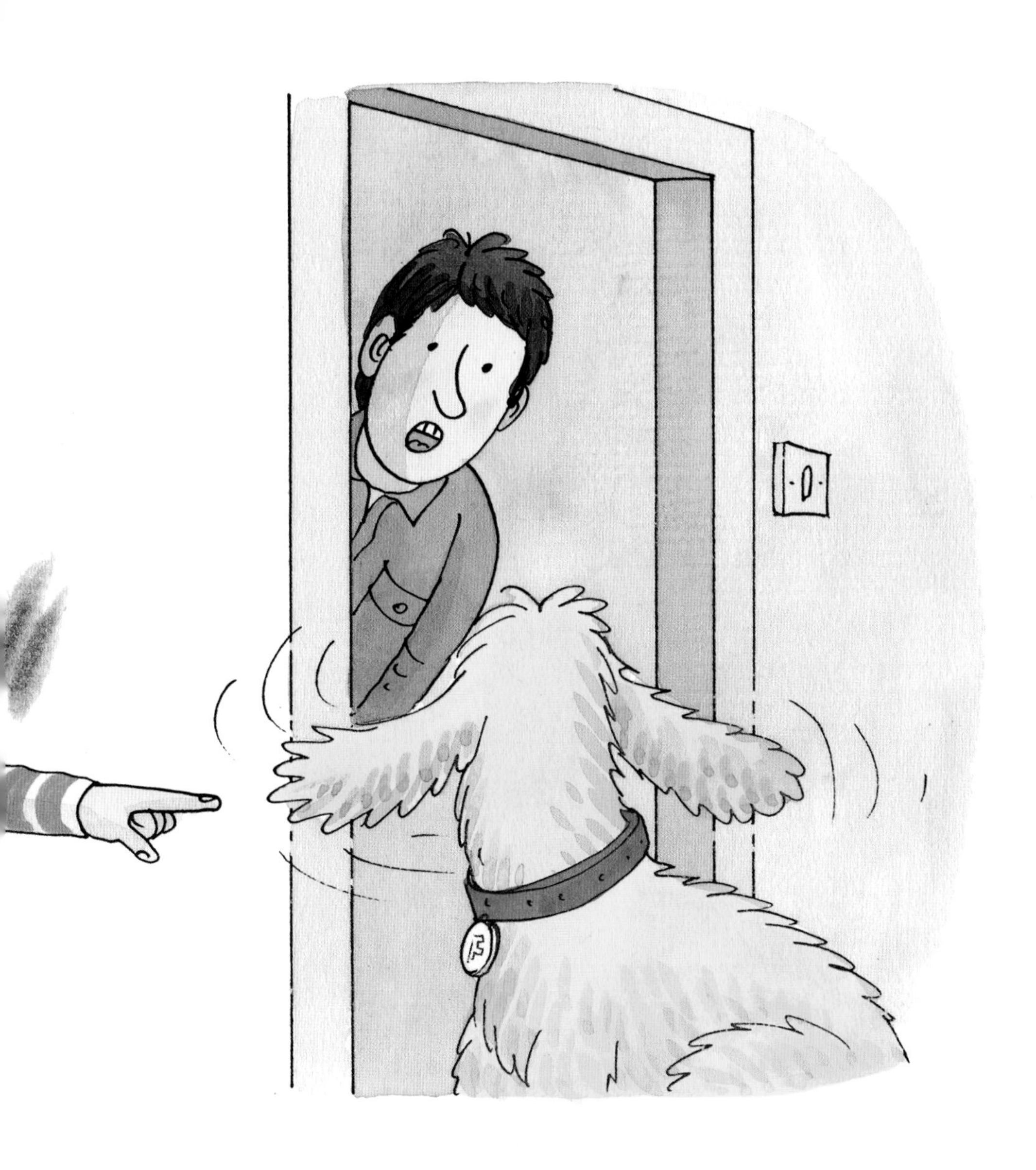

"It wasn't Floppy," said Dad.

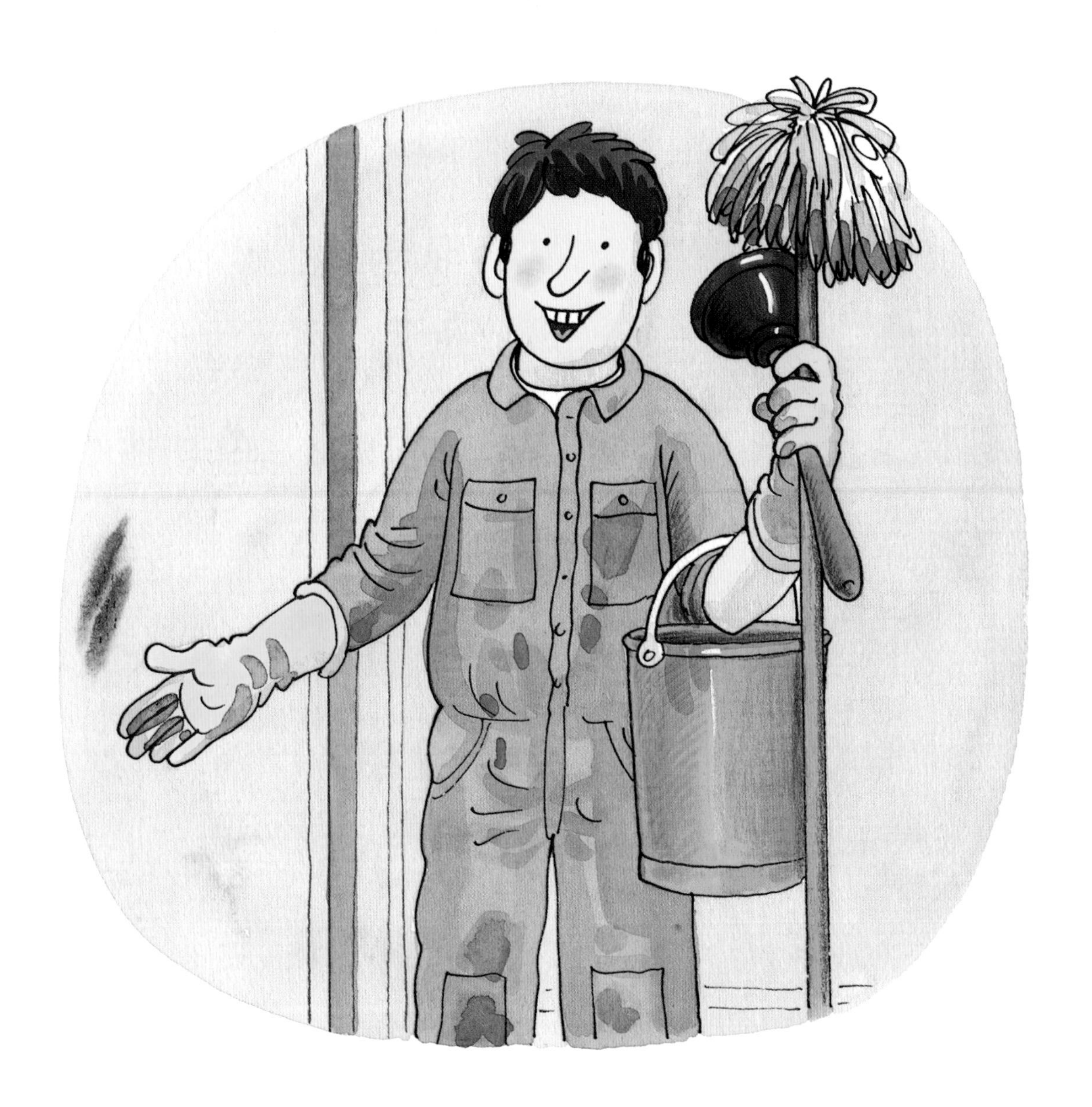

"It was me."